the Institute
of Management
F O U N D A T I O N

The Institute of Management (IM) exists to promote the development, exercise and recognition of professional management. The Institute embraces all levels of management from student to chief executive and supports its own Foundation which provides a unique portfolio of services for all managers, enabling them to develop skills and achieve management excellence.

For information on the various levels and benefits of membership, please contact:

Department HS
Institute of Management
Cottingham Road
Corby
Northants NN17 1TT

Tel. 01536 204222
Fax 01536 201651

This series is commissioned by the Institute of Management Foundation.

CONTENTS

Successful
Stress
Management
in a week

ALISON STRAW &
CARY COOPER

Hodder & Stoughton

A MEMBER OF THE HODDER HEADLINE GROUP

Order queries: please contact Bookpoint Ltd, 39 Milton Park, Abingdon, Oxon
OX14 4TD. Telephone: (44) 01235 400414, Fax: (44) 01235 400454. Lines are
open from 9.00 – 6.00, Monday to Saturday, with a 24 hour message
answering service. Email address: orders@bookpoint.co.uk

British Library Cataloguing in Publication Data
A catalogue record for this title is available from The British Library

ISBN 0 340 712015

First published 1993
Second edition 1998
Impression number 10 9   8 7   6 5 4 3 2 1
Year   2003 2002 2001 2000 1999   1998

Cover photo from Telegraph Photo Library

Typeset by Multiplex Techniques Ltd, St Mary Cray, Kent.
Printed in Great Britain for Hodder & Stoughton Educational, a division of
Hodder Headline Plc, 338 Euston Road, London NW1 3BH by
Cox and Wyman, Reading, Berkshire.

Stress as a word is now firmly embedded in our vocabulary. In the course of a week it would not be unusual to hear stress used to describe a wide range of feelings, symptoms and situations:

'I feel stressed' – describing the rush and panic in meeting a deadline.

'They're under a lot of stress' – offered as an explanation for a colleague's unusual irritability or their uncharacteristic behaviour.

'It's a stressful job' – awarding a specific job an odd sort of status.

The experience of stress is very personal. Pressures come from many different directions, affecting us in different ways and at different times. In some situations when we are under an enormous amount of pressure, we cope, are stimulated and on occasions positively thrive. In other situations we may suffer in some way, show signs of not coping and feel unable to meet either the deadlines or the expectations.

Recognising the sources of such pressures and developing strategies to cope with and prevent them can relieve us of much stress.

This book is a practical guide, written in the format of a week. By putting aside some time each day, starting on Sunday, by the end of the week you will be able to answer some of the questions you may have on stress. This will help you in two ways – personally and in your role as a manager.

The symptoms of stress

Before we can deal with stress in ourselves and others, we must recognise when and in what situations it occurs.

Today, therefore, we will look at the symptoms which can alert us to the fact that we may be under stress.

The word 'symptom' is often associated with a medical setting; we know that if we sneeze, it may be the symptom of a cold, allergy or a whole range of other things. However, diagnosing a condition from symptoms can be difficult. The symptoms of stress can be:

- physical
- behavioural
- workplace

These symptoms are often linked and develop over time to the point where they become difficult to distinguish from normal behaviour. Any of the following symptoms can indicate a degree of stress which, if left unresolved, might have serious implications.

Physical symptoms

The physical symptoms of stress may include:

- Fast breathing
- Dry mouth and throat
- Clammy hands

- Feeling hot
- Tense muscles
- Indigestion
- Diarrhoea 腹泻
- Constipation 便秘
- Undue exhaustion 过度疲机
- Tension headaches 紧张头痛
- Nervous twitching 神经抽动
- Fidgeting 烦躁

Of course, each of these may be experienced in normal life, as a result of normal physical effort, external temperature or too much food and drink. They become symptoms of stress when they do not have an obvious cause, when several of them come at the same time, or when we experience them more often than we would expect.

The symptoms arise because the body believes it is preparing itself for immediate action. It is preparing us to either 'fight', in what may be a life or death struggle, or for the dash to safety, 'flight' – responses usually more appropriate in the jungle than our office!

Whether in fight or flight the body automatically: releases adrenalin into the bloodstream, shuts down the digestive system, thickens the blood so that it will clot and pumps blood more quickly around the body.

These responses were designed to be short-lived – to get us away from or to overcome the source of potential danger. Prolonged exposure to stress may make us more vulnerable to: stomach and intestinal problems, skin problems and heart disease.

Behavioural symptoms

There are many behavioural symptoms of stress, which include:

Feeling:
- upset, worried and tearful
- irritated by others
- misunderstood
- powerless
- unable to cope
- restless
- a failure
- unattractive
- demotivated

You may recognise such signs either in yourself or others, without being aware of the other ways in which stress affects you. You may find that you are becoming frustrated, angry and clumsy or that you are waking at regular intervals in the night, thinking about work. You may have difficulty concentrating, thinking clearly or making decisions. Or, you may experience a loss of creativity or a diminishing interest in both yourself and others. It may also be that you become aware of increasing your alcohol consumption, smoking or eating, or the converse – losing your appetite.

The way we respond to stress varies depending on our personality, early upbringing and life experiences. Everyone has their own pattern of stress response, so the warning signs may vary, as may their intensity. Some people know their own pattern of stress response and can gauge the depth of the problem by the nature and severity of their own symptoms or changes in behaviour.

One of the most obvious signs to be aware of is the intensification of your personality traits.

People who are:
- careful become overmeticulous
- anxious become panic-stricken
- insecure become vulnerable
- irritable become explosive

To identify these reactions you will need to become more aware of how you feel in particular situations. Beware of the following:

Typical reactions
- Irritability
- Anger and aggression
- Anxiety
- Depression
- Swings of mood
- Withdrawal

Workplace symptoms

We spend a major part of our waking lives at work and if we are under stress, symptoms can effect us in the workplace, often in the following ways:

- Lower job satisfaction
- Reduced job performance
- Loss of vitality and energy
- Communication breakdown
- Poor decision making
- Reduced creativity and innovation
- Focus on unproductive tasks

All of the above need to be viewed in relation to the previous or normal quality of your work and interactions. Most commonly, stress will lessen your satisfaction with work and reduce your performance.

Whilst you are not performing as well as you might as a result of stress, the pressures and demands on you remain the same. To prevent getting too far behind you begin to take more work home and you may begin to feel very tired. You don't have the time or energy to take part in your normal leisure activities and your home life also begins to suffer. Before you know it, you have become trapped in a downward spiral of problems.

By recognising and acknowledging these changes you can forestall some of the more long-term consequences of stress in your workplace behaviour.

These consequences can be viewed in terms of the health, performance and productivity of the individual. There are also other costs, to organisations and to the economy as a whole.

It is estimated that in Britain at least 40 million working days are lost each year due to the effects of stress, costing British industry in the region of £7 billion.

It is important to recognise that our bodies can cope with occasional episodes of stress, and these usually do little harm. However, in today's society stressful situations often follow in quick succession with little or no time for recovery, or are extended over long periods of time. When this occurs there may be serious consequences.

Worrying about these consequences may seem like a potent source of stress in itself. However, we must remember that they are only likely to operate as the result of long-term exposure to severe, unresolved stress.

After reading this book, you should be much less liable to such dangers!

Exploring your symptoms checklist

1 What do you recognise as the symptoms of stress for you?

2 Think about situations and experiences you have had which you would describe as stressful:
   • How did you feel?

   • How did you behave?

   • How did it affect your work?

By learning to recognise your own symptoms and pattern of stress response you will be able to gauge the depth of your problems and develop positive strategies to manage them.

Just as damage from stress initially affects the individual, the causes and the process of learning to cope with stress begin at an individual level. We will begin to take you through this process tomorrow, by identifying some of the potential causes of stress at work.

The workplace causes of stress

Work occupies a major part of our lives, both in terms of time and the importance we place on it.

How often, when introduced to someone, is our first question, 'What do you do?'. We make judgements and award status on the basis of people's occupation. Work is a major source of self-esteem. We meet people through work, make friends and develop contacts. Work also provides the income on which we and our families depend. It is therefore not surprising that for many, work is of central importance.

Work is also a source of great satisfaction and challenge. However, it can contain potentially harmful elements. You may already have identified your work as stressful and described it as such. By the end of today, you will be clearer in identifying the causes of that stress.

Some occupations have been found to be more stressful than others. Stress league tables have been drawn up to compare broad occupational categories. However, comparisons such as these can be misleading – jobs change and so do occupational pressures.

It is also inaccurate to suggest that stress is a problem exclusive to certain occupations, nor is stress the prerogative of either high or low status workers, or even solely associated with work – **anyone** can experience stress.

There are common workplace causes, which can be broken down into the following areas:

- Factors related to the job
- Role in the organisation
- Relationships at work
- Career development
- Organisational change

We will look at each of these individually for the rest of today.

Factors related to the job

There are many factors intrinsic to the job itself which can have an impact on an individual's stress, including:

- Environment
- Travel
- Technology
- Pressure

Environment
The environment in which we work has an impact on how we are able to perform in a particular role. It is, however, an element of work that can be overlooked.

The term 'poor working conditions' can conjure up an image of heavy industry, dangerous situations and other outdoor and physically strenuous activities, where the work and environment interface is obvious. We rarely associate 'poor working conditions' with deskbound jobs or those involved with the management of people or things.

However, there are many aspects of the everyday working environment which may contribute to stress.

It may be that you consider yourself an organised person, whose desk is always tidy and ordered. But on looking round, you may become aware that your desk is like an island and you are surrounded by untidiness and clutter. Over time you have become used to this environment. But an environment that doesn't fit with you can affect your work, your mood and your overall well-being.

One manager, having become stressed for no apparent reason, decided to change the dark colour of his office. Following this and the addition of some pictures the difference was only too apparent. Instead of the dreary, dull and dark room he had a bright and fresh environment to help him cope with the other demands of the day.

Our role also can affect the environment in which we work. For example, following a promotion to a new department, one manager was awarded the ultimate benefit, in the eyes of the directors – an office. However, both the office and the quiet environment began to feel like a sentence of solitary confinement. The manager missed the noise and busyness of the open plan office, the opportunities to bounce ideas off colleagues and the mutual support. The environment fitted the role but not the individual.

Think about your work environment. Throughout the week, become aware of the situations in which you thrive and those which adversely affect you.

The example below illustrates how a change in role caused illness for one particular manager:

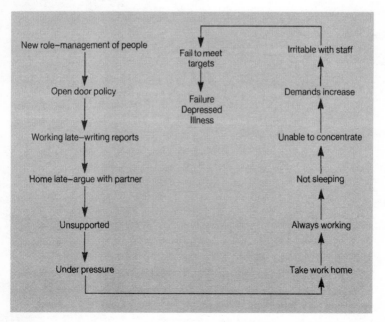

Only after an illness did this manager begin to see how oppressive work had become and to understand that she could instigate the change necessary. The change for her was to create undisturbed time and space in normal working hours. This illustrates how, by simply paying attention to the demands of your role and your needs, you can influence the environment and as a result manage the stress successfully.

Travel
Travel falls into two categories: travel to and from work – 'commuting' – and travel for work.

Commuting frequently represents a major cause of stress, especially from the delays and difficulties so often experienced, whatever the means of travel.

Driving in particular has its own associated problems, such as:

- Traffic
- Weather
- Road conditions
- Navigating
- Getting lost
- Car trouble
- Vibration
- Tiredness

Public transport, whilst generally less stressful, may present its own unique stressors. If you have been delayed on a train journey or your plane has not arrived on time, you will have experienced a whole range of emotions which may have included anger, frustration, anxiety or confusion.

These stem from a lack of:

- **control** – over the situation
- **clarity** – about the cause of the delay
- **understanding** – as to how it will be resolved
- **communication** – you may not be able to contact those that may be expecting you at your destination

Travelling for work can often appear glamourous, particularly to those who are deskbound. However, travelling long distances to unknown places, often alone, tired, with limited time to make the cultural adaptations necessary, can present stress factors as well as challenges.

Technology

The introduction of new technology into the workplace has required employees to adapt to new environments, systems and ways of working. Once the necessary adaptations have been made, keeping up with new technology can be an added pressure in an already busy schedule, which can lead to an overload.

Think back to a situation when you were learning a new skill and remember how clumsy and incompetent you felt. When new technology is introduced, in a way it's much like beginning again but it has an added dimension as you often need to 'unlearn' skills, which can lead to you becoming very conscious of your incompetence. For some, this can be a challenge; however, for others it may prove too big an adaptation or serve to reinforce their existing feelings of incompetence.

Pressure

Work with overwhelming time pressures and demanding deadlines can create stress, depending on how well and to what extent you feel your skills and abilities are being used.

There are two different sources of work pressure:

- Too much work
- Poor skills match

The symptoms of too much work are the easiest to identify; you may need to work long hours or it may be that you find it increasingly difficult to differentiate between work and home. Such pressures can also be self-imposed, by:

- setting unrealistic goals
- not delegating
- attempting to change too much too quickly

The matching of people to roles is also essential. When the job demands are below your capabilities, you may find the work boring, not stimulating and unchallenging. On the other hand the job may call for knowledge or skills you do not at present possess. In both situations, the result may be:

- low self-esteem and confidence
- lack of commitment and motivation
- being easily diverted

Pressure can also relate to the type of job, as some jobs have a high exposure to pressure and therefore risk of stress. If you recall from yesterday, the stress response is intended to be short-lived, but people in high risk jobs have a constant exposure to stress.

This exposure is similar to the experience of an athlete at the beginning of a race. The official goes through a process of preparing all the athletes for the split second that they need to 'go'. The experience of those in the high risk groups is similar to an athlete being 'on their marks'.

To those in the high risk groups, this is a way of life and a factor intrinsic to the job, which is reflected in the training and support they receive. However, for many others the 'on your marks' situation is a common feature of their response to their work environment, but often without an understanding of how to manage and minimise such stress. Imagine yourself holding the 'on your marks' position for a day, a week or longer and the damaging effects that would have!

Role in the organisation

There is a tendency to think of stress as applying only to busy executives, who are constantly resolving problems and making decisions. However, such people may sometimes experience less stress than those below them.

This is because they can control much of their working lives. Being able to make decisions and prioritise, results in less stress than not being in control.

There can be other problems associated with role:

'I was called into the office yesterday. I always think the worst, but it was good news; they want me to develop a new department. When I first came out of the meeting I felt relief and a sense of recognition. Now all I seem to be feeling is a sense of panic. I don't know where to start. It doesn't seem as if they are clear about the department's function or my role. I kept asking questions, but they said these were issues I would be expected to resolve and they had confidence in my judgement. I just don't know where to start, I'm not sure I can do it anyway.'

This situation illustrates how a lack of clarity about the particular scope of the role and responsibilities can affect someone. The range of emotions described is vast and it may seem contradictory to feel isolated and frightened whilst also challenged and stimulated. However, it is just this range of emotions which can lead to stress.

Your own role may require you to have responsibility for people, budgets, buildings or projects. All of these can bring their own particular stressors because they are dependent on other unpredictable factors, such as:

- relationships
- market forces
- economy
- environment

Your role in the organisation can also create a form of conflict. It is not uncommon to find yourself in a situation where you are torn by conflicting job demands; doing things that you don't want to, that you believe are not your job, or having more tasks or projects given to you than you feel is reasonable. You may not be sure whether to maintain the status quo and respond to the demands, putting yourself under more pressure, or challenge them. Both strategies are risky!

Relationships within the organisation

Relationships with other people can be a major source of both stress and support at work.

When the relationship with superiors is good, there is an atmosphere of warmth, friendship and mutual trust. However, if the converse is true, superiors are likely to be:

- critical
- unapproachable
- uninterested
- distant

The same can be true of relationships with subordinates.

Relationships within the organisation can be a source of great satisfaction. Many strong and lasting friendships are made as a result of a working relationship.

Take a moment to think of friendships that have stemmed from a work relationship. The basis of this relationship may have been shared:

- likes
- interests
- goals
- values

It is likely that in such cases there is mutual trust and respect.

However, a shared office, responsibility for task or secretarial support can be a source of stress, if your relationship with the other party is not good.

Good working relationships promote effective communication and leave less room for ambiguity. Relationships are essential to our well-being. However, working relationships are often the hardest to deal with.

Career development

In the early stages of our careers we may be rewarded by significant progression through and sometimes out of organisations, shown by salary rises and promotion. However, as careers continue, opportunities often become fewer, progress becomes slower and eventually stops. Such restriction can thwart ambition and can become a major cause of stress as there is little to achieve in terms of money, status or new challenges.

The contraction of working life, the threat of obsolescence or lack of favour creates a vulnerability that can lead to stress.

Organisational change

The organisation, its culture and climate can have a profound effect on individuals and their sense of well-being.

Being part of an organisation can present threats to an individual's sense of freedom, autonomy and security. In a static or slowly evolving situation, the threat is lessened. However, major changes within the organisation can prove stressful, such as:

- closure of a site
- relocation
- redundancies
- restructuring
- merger or takeover

Individuals within organisations need to feel a sense of belonging. A commonly expressed complaint by employees is that they are 'not included in consultations' and that there are 'few opportunities to participate'. When such complaints are listened to and acted on, individuals begin to feel an integral part of the whole and more committed, which is demonstrated by an improvement in communications and greater productivity.

All change also involves loss. However desirable or necessary the end result of change, it will result in a loss of familiar:

- faces
- places
- pleasures
- ways of doing things
- organisational supports

In times of recession, the threat to individuals is worsened by a real or perceived sense of insecurity. Those who are not threatened directly with job loss may be affected in terms of their attitudes, confidence and performance. There will be fewer opportunities to develop. Training budgets are often the first to be cut, fewer new jobs will be available and frozen budgets will place severe limits on many kinds of development.

Workplace stress checklist

Look down the following list, identifying which cause stress in your work situation, rating them on a scale of 1–10 (1 = highest, 10 = lowest)

Factors related to the job	Heavy workload
	Work environment
	Travel
	Danger
	Technology
Role in the organisation	Clarity with role
	Authority
	Control
Relationships at work	Feedback
	Conflict
	Support
	Praise
	Recognition
Career development	Security
	Opportunities
	Interest
Organisational change	Inability to influence
	Change of style
	Threats

Before we finish today, there is another side to work which must not be overlooked. Because work can be an integral part of the process of coping with life stress, it can have a positive as well as a negative effect.

Work is an important part of our lives. It is a source of:

- income
- self-esteem
- development

It can also be a form of coping and refuge. For example, someone coping with a major loss in their life may focus on their work to cope with their loneliness and depression.

We end today with a cautionary note. Having identified the workplace symptoms yesterday and the causes today, do not automatically assume that the symptoms are a reflection of workplace stressors. The demands on us are never that straightforward. It is important, therefore, to identify the source of the stress and differentiate between work factors and those in our lives generally.

To help you with this process, tomorrow we will focus on the potential sources of life stress.

Sources of life stress

We live in an ever-changing world, and must constantly adapt and adjust to both technological and social changes.

In addition to these changes, there are the recurring pressures which form a fairly predictable pattern of events during our lives. Potentially, these events are sources of both stress and satisfaction, their common feature being that they require us to make some adjustment. It is these that we will identify today.

By focusing on two stages – childhood and adulthood – we will identify the range of situations experienced and the potential for both stress and satisfaction.

From childhood to adulthood

These formative years are recognised as the most important in our lives. Childhood is a time of developing relationships, learning, rewards, punishments, disappointments and achievements. It is, above all, a time of meeting one's own and others' expectations.

Today, social pressures affect children from an early age. Because a wider range of choices are open to them, both at school and at home, they must face a wider range of decisions.

The biggest potential stressors during this period are the expectations of significant people in their lives:

- parents
- teachers
- peer groups

Problems arise because the expectations of these groups are so different and sometimes contradictory. Children can therefore experience difficulty in choosing appropriate behaviour in varying situations with different groups of people.

With adolescence, the potential demands, and therefore the stressors, increase. The transition from childhood to adolescence is itself often turbulent due to the combination of physical, psychological and environmental changes.

Perhaps the most significant and traumatic transition is from school to work. At this stage young people are trying to prove themselves as adults and gain recognition from others, whilst still needing the psychological rewards and securities of childhood. In the world of work these rewards may be expressed by:

- praise
- promotion
- salary increases
- greater responsibility

However, if they are not quickly forthcoming, this can create difficulties and stress.

The young person often faces other unfamiliar situations, all of which require major readjustment, such as:

- living alone
- finding a partner
- maintaining a relationship
- budgeting
- establishing a home

It is the connection between these life events and the necessary adjustments that we will focus on for the remainder of today.

In the late 1960s, Dr Thomas Holmes and Dr Richard Rahe devised one of the major research projects of their time. They questioned several hundred people to establish which events that occurred during their life required the most readjustment. As a result, the following scale of life events was developed. The higher the score, the more stressful the event. Study the list and mark those that you have experienced in the last year.

Life events

Death of a partner	100
Divorce	73
Separation from partner	65
Jail sentence	63
Death of a close family member	63
Personal injury or illness	53
Marriage	50
Loss of job	47
Reconciliation with a partner	45
Retirement	45
Change in your health	44
Pregnancy	40
Sexual difficulties	39
New family member	39
Major business or work changes	39
Change in your financial state	38
Death of a close friend	37
Arguments with a partner	35
Large mortgage	31
Foreclosure of a mortgage or loan	30
Change in responsibilities at work	29
Son or daughter leaving home	29
Trouble with in-laws	29
Outstanding personal achievement	28
Partner beginning or stopping work	26
Child starts or ends school	26
Change in living conditions	25
Change in personal habits	24
Trouble with boss or employer	23
Change in working hours or conditions	20
Change in residence	20

Change in schools	20
Change in social activities	18
Low mortgage or loan	17
Change in sleeping habits	16
Change in number of family gatherings	15
Change in eating habits	15
Holidays	13
Christmas	12
Minor violations of the law	11

Holmes and Rahe, 'The Social Adjustment Scale', 1969

By totalling the value of events you will get some indication of how much stress you may be experiencing. If your score is over 250, you have obviously undergone some major changes in your life; you will find it helpful to study Thursday's chapter to help you manage the effects of this change.

It is also interesting to note that situations at home are more stressful than those at work. The scale also demonstrates the importance of the cumulative effects of the events that you have experienced. Perhaps the most surprising thing to some is that pleasant events can bring with them added pressures.

We will now look in more detail at three specific events from the listing to highlight the potential for stress:

- Relationships
- Illness
- Holidays

Relationships

It is interesting to note that of the top ten scoring life events, only one relates to work and five out of the ten relate to relationships.

Stress in relationships can be caused by differing or conflicting expectations, roles and needs. You may have experienced these and relate to them. We will take marriage as an example, however, this could as easily relate to any long-term relationship.

The early days of marriage may be a happy and fulfilling time for both partners. However, there will also be the need for major adjustments. Both partners and their respective families often have high expectations, and these can become a source of stress.

In today's society traditional roles are less well defined. Increasingly women go out to work and are therefore not financially dependent on men. This has led to the development of other, less traditional, patterns in marriages and long term partnerships. These changing expectations and roles of men and women may create a situation in which partners struggle to maintain a relationship.

Patterns have emerged which highlight the potential sources and causes of stress in marriage.

Traditionally, the pattern was of a caring wife and homemaker and a husband as the breadwinner. In this situation, the husband and wife shared common goals, their roles were clear and the occasions for stress resulting from conflicting expectations fewer.

However, economic pressures and the social and psychological need to develop their own identity have resulted in women taking a more active role outside the home, by either pursuing a full-time career or education. The pace of these changes has not been matched by changes in the pressures on women as carers and sources of support. This can create stress, especially if their partners do not support their choices and preferred lifestyle.

The pattern of a dual career family unit in particular can create stressors for both partners.

For example, a committed and busy couple, with somewhat chaotic domestic arrangements, may experience conflict as to who plays the principal role with the advent of children.

Children can be a major source of stress. The need and desire to spend time with and enjoy the company of one's children, as well as concerns over their health, education and safety and other aspects of bringing them up can often be a leading stress factor for either or both parents.

Traditional units can also create stress. One partner may need and depend on the caring and supportive aspects of the relationship. Their job may demand a total commitment from both partners and involve relocating at regular intervals. This can create stress, as one partner has little control. The other partner may also not be happy with the situation, feeling guilty at the disruption their job is causing the whole family unit.

Stress can be the cause of problems as well as the result of problems. For example, stress can cause sexual problems. Sexual problems can also create additional stress.

Marriages have a life-cycle of their own and adjustments are needed constantly. When individual needs and aspirations change and the pattern of the relationship remains the same, the situation will result in stress. There is a need for the respective partners to be aware of, negotiate and adjust to change.

Relationships may also be affected by factors such as:

- debt
- where we live

Many people will face money worries owing to inflation, high mortgages or an overcommitment to credit. This problem creates associated worries such as how to keep the house, or requires people to dig deeper into savings to keep ahead of bills. This can act as a source of stress and, in conjunction with other work or home stress, can cause mental or physical ill health.

Where we live also has a significant effect on our coping resources. Some people choose to live in urban or city environments where the noise, polluted air and cramped environment may not relieve the stress from home or work. On the other hand, those who choose to live a distance from their workplace, perhaps in a more rural environment, have the added stress of commuting to and from work.

Many people have no choice where they live. In consequence, they may suffer from stress factors common to areas of high unemployment and poverty such as bad community relations, violence, theft and an overall sense of insecurity.

A strong supportive relationship is crucial in managing emotional stress of any kind. The stability that such a positive relationship provides can support individuals when they are faced with even the most critical of events in their lives. Marriage or a long term relationship can be seen as both a resource and a burden. Moreover, how we see it can affect what we get out of it.

Illness

That illness is a major source of stress is hardly surprising due to the major consequences of many illnesses and the fatal nature of some. However, many people have exaggerated fears about illness, because of lack of knowledge or reluctance to ask questions. When questions are asked, the explanation may not be properly understood.

It is common to hear people say, 'I haven't got the time to be ill' or 'I can't afford to be ill'. We don't plan for illness and often prefer not to think about it at all. Thus, when we are faced with an illness the level of readjustment can be massive. We find we are unable to control our life fully and a sense of dependency creeps in, whether on doctors, family or friends.

Life threatening illnesses are particularly stressful, not only because of the prospect of pain and disability but because of the fear of the unknown. Also, the realisation of our own mortality is inevitably stressful, bringing a whole range of emotions such as fear, sadness, guilt, anger, regret and disappointment.

Holidays

At the other extreme, holidays are identified as a potential stressor. Holidays should ideally be relaxing and recuperative. However, they can sometimes turn into an event that is anything but!

The pressure to do things together as a family unit can create tension and arguments. Living with your partner and other family members 24 hours a day is often unfamiliar and stressful. On a foreign holiday the loss of everyday control over food, money, language, etc. can create a situation where tension mounts and tempers erupt. The loss of the familiar and soothing routines and surroundings of our everyday life can cause stress. The return to them after several weeks of absence can be even more traumatic.

Coping with life events

Some events on the list are unpredictable and we have no control over them, such as illness or personal injury. Others are brought on by choice such as a holiday, taking out a new loan or moving house to a property with a higher mortgage.

Troubles often start when too many life events occur at once, as any individual can only handle a limited number of changes at any one time. Therefore, when there is a predictable life event looming, you should try not to make things worse by introducing other changes. Too many events during a short period can overtax our adaptive and coping resources and this can lead to stress and possibly ill health.

Life events checklist

Assess the impact of one recent significant life event on you and your life, by ticking the appropriate column:

	High	**Medium**	**Low**
Job performance			
Relationships at home			
Relationships at work			
Physical well-being			
Emotional well-being			

By being more aware of the dangers we are better able to take precautions or actions to prevent or cope with them.

Most events, however, are neutral; how we respond to them depends on our lifestyle and what else is going on. Tomorrow we will focus on how our lifestyle affects our coping capabilities.

What is your lifestyle?

We have already identified that our lives can be a rich mixture of happiness, strain and pressure, brought about by events and situations. We are all confronted daily with potentially stressful situations, so why is it that some individuals may appear to have an undue share of problems?

Today, we will focus on you and your lifestyle and the ways in which these can influence and affect your vulnerability to stress:

Your lifestyle
- Personality
- Strategies
- Characteristics
- Support

Personality

Next time you visit a supermarket, look around at the queues of waiting shoppers. They may fall into one of the two following categories.

For some people waiting, their impatience is clear. They:

- shuffle their feet
- strain to see what is happening ahead
- sigh in exasperation
- look angrily at the checkout operator
- move between queues

Others seem unconcerned about the wait. They:

- enjoy the chance of a pause
- use the time to catch up on other things
- are interested in the flow of life around them
- pick up a magazine to glance through

People in the first category are experiencing anxiety and distress; those in the second category have developed mechanisms that help them cope with stress in such situations.

There are other more serious consequences for those in the first category. Research suggests that they have both a higher incidence of, and susceptibility to, coronary heart disease. So, faced with the same situation, why do people react so differently?

Studies of coronary patients have found that they display certain common characteristics and behave in similar ways. They are:

- competitive
- aggressive
- hasty
- impatient
- restless

This type of lifestyle and behaviour, has been labelled Type 'A'. Look at the following paragraphs and see if you can recognise someone who matches this behaviour. It may be you! (This is drawn from Friedman and Rosenman's book, *Type A Behaviour and Your Heart*.)

Competitive
Such people often see themselves in terms of what they can achieve, own and win.

They tend to talk in these terms, frequently using words such as beat, best, biggest. They are unable to relax from their constant search for alternative methods of jumping, beating and avoiding.

Competition becomes compulsive; even the supermarket queue becomes a competitive challenge, as they strive to identify the quickest route through the checkout.

Aggressive
They challenge and confront others regularly, especially those like them. They have aggressive mannerisms and particularly explosive speech patterns. Their aggression is also evident in their physical stance, they often have tense facial muscles and they are prepared to 'fight'.

Hasty
They have a chronic sense of urgency, attempting to do two or more things at the same time, scheduling more and more into less and less time.

They become easily irritated and angry over trivial happenings and the mistakes of others, never appreciating or even noticing when things are going well. They are typically egocentric, focused inward, on their own wants, needs and wishes.

Impatient
They feel and reveal to others an impatience with the rate of most events, by typically moving, walking and eating rapidly. Even in conversations they can reveal this, by 'accentuating key words in their ordinary speech', or 'speaking very fast with a tendency to utter the last few words of a sentence more rapidly'. They may also find it difficult to restrain from hurrying the speech of others.

Restless

They spend very little time relaxing, may feel guilty when trying to relax, and never have time to spare to be with friends or family. This restlessness and impatience may also be indicated by characteristic gestures such as drumming fingers, tapping feet or nervous tics.

Therefore wasting time in queues, as in the first example, is something that a Type 'A' cannot stand, as they are being held up and having valuable time taken away from them. In fact, any form of waste they find irritating.

They will often say, 'I thrive on stress'. Stress can be seen as a form of addiction, which produces a feeling of confidence and elation, but often leads to them seeking out more challenging situations to maintain this state.

Not surprisingly, Type 'A' individuals are deeply involved in and committed to their work – they are often labelled as workaholics. Other areas of their life, such as family and friends, are relatively neglected. As a result, they may suffer marital and social relationship problems, as they struggle for success and need to work longer and longer hours to achieve their goals.

Type 'A's seem to have two typical responses:

- speeding up
- doing more than one thing at a time

They find it difficult to believe that their way of behaving is counterproductive. Such self-induced stress often distorts their perception and they fail to recognise what is happening to them and those around them.

This stereotyped picture of Type 'A' behaviour is not an attractive one. It may be one that you wouldn't like to associate yourself with. Or you may accept the diagnosis, but believe you will be the one to survive and reach the top. Some feel that this is the way they are and have to be and there is nothing they can do about it.

There are positive aspects to Type 'A' behaviour, as such people often have a high degree of mental and physical alertness and can accomplish a great deal, carrying others along with their enthusiasm and drive.

There is also a link between high status jobs and this type of behaviour, but it is important to recognise that it can damage your health!

However, it would be misleading to suggest that it is only a competitive, rushed, aggressive person who gets things done. The alternative behaviour – Type 'B' – can achieve as much, but in different and less stressful ways.

Type 'B' behaviour is found in the group less susceptible to heart disease. They are typically:

- free of the habits and traits of Type 'A'
- not suffering urgency and impatience
- harbouring no free-floating hostility
- without need to impress others with achievements
- playing in order to find relaxation and fun
- able to work without agitation
- able to relax without guilt

These distinctions provide clues to stress prone personalities. However, it is wrong to suggest that we exhibit either one or the other type of behaviour, exclusively.

So let's look at other characteristics which will help us to understand the links between illness and personality.

You may find it helpful to think about the following themes:

- Commitment
- Control
- Challenge

These three 'C's together form what is referred to by Suzanne Kobasa as the 'Hardy Personality' and are common characteristics in those who are found to be less liable to ill health.

Commitment
'Committed' individuals place a great importance on, and interest in, who they are and what they are doing. Such people have a tendency to involve themselves fully in many situations, including work, family, interpersonal relationships and institutions. They lead balanced and fulfilling lives. Their 'commitment' to their preferred way of life and value system is total and can be contagious. They have commitment to what they do and feel confident about their abilities.

Control
An individual in 'control' believes and acts as if they can influence the course of events. They may seek explanations as to why something is happening, but tend to take responsibility upon themselves for the course of events rather than viewing situations as another's responsibility or beyond their control.

'Hardy' individuals take control over situations in which they find themselves. With this control they are better able to make decisions and take positive action to influence the outcome. Those that do not believe they have control and have little influence upon situations are more likely to become resigned to the role of passive participant in the process.

Challenge

'Hardy' individuals have a basic sense of purpose which allows them to tolerate a wide range of experiences, knowing that they have the resources to respond positively to them. They recognise that change is an ingredient of normal life.

They are people who are able to see threats as challenges and changes as fresh opportunities. They turn stressful life events into possibilities and opportunities for personal growth, development or benefit. Such people seek stimulation, change and opportunities for openness, with a willingness to experiment.

Those who lack hardiness may display alienation, powerlessness or insecurity. They feel threatened in the face of change.

Personality checklist

Mark on the lines below the position which you feel is a true reflection of how you respond to everyday events:

Competitive	_____	Non-competitive
Aggressive	_____	Submissive
Hasty	_____	Considered
Impatient	_____	Tolerant
Restless	_____	Relaxed

Do you normally feel:

Powerless	_____	In control
Outsider	_____	You belong
Threatened	_____	Challenged

Strategies

So far today we have focused on how you respond – the type of person you are. From your reading on previous days, you may have decided you want to make changes to minimise stress in your life. Developing appropriate skills, strategies and techniques is essential to this process.

You can, for example, deal directly with a situation by seeking and implementing solutions. If this succeeds, the result is a sense of well-earned achievement, which helps you to prepare for situations in the future. However, inappropriate coping strategies will add to the stress.

We will look at a range of these coping strategies in more detail tomorrow.

Characteristics

The degree to which an event is perceived as a threat can depend on a number of characteristics, such as:

- age
- gender
- sexuality
- religious beliefs
- disabilities
- race

For example, a young and confident manager may see an approaching merger as an opportunity, whereas an older manager may view it as a potential threat and therefore much more stressful. Individuals deal with threats very differently, ranging from feeling and becoming isolated to feeling strong through the support of others like themselves.

Support

As was discussed on Monday, a positive and nurturing support group such as family, friends and co-workers can help to offset the effects of stress.

The feelings of acceptance, belonging, shoulders to cry on and ears to listen can be of enormous help, even if the actual cause of stress remains.

Each individual meets the challenges of everyday life with a complex set of physical and emotional characteristics, coping styles, values and history.

Tomorrow, we will start to explore how to move from your current lifestyle to your preferred lifestyle, using your resources to cope with stress in a productive and creative way.

Helping yourself

So far this week, we have focused on recognising symptoms and identifying sources. An understanding of both of these is essential to the helping strategies we begin to look at today.

We all develop coping strategies for situations we frequently meet. Life would be impossible if we did not. However, the effectiveness of our strategies varies. Some may work well. Others, however, may be damaging and serve as a block to our further development. Before moving on today, we will identify some common blocks that you may recognise in yourself. All have a common theme – they are **not** concerned with changing the situation but justify its existence.

Denying
We can explain our behaviour or the long hours we work with rational answers. Finding what appear acceptable reasons for our conduct in an attempt to convince both listeners and ourselves. Denying that the problem exists, in an attempt to persuade others as well as ourselves that nothing is wrong.

Distancing
Attributing our shortcomings and failures to the environment and others. Distancing ourselves from the problem and projecting it somewhere else, or onto someone else. As a result, our perception of the situation changes, so that we then no longer feel responsible for it or indeed for dealing with it.

Displacing
Having less time and energy for things that are central to
our well-being such as friends and family. Most commonly,
individuals become solely focused on work and begin to
displace their emotional emphasis and energy from family
and friends to work and colleagues.

Withdrawing
Feeling we have no control over the situation and retiring or
withdrawing emotionally from it. This often results from
the failure of other strategies.

None of these help. They may be summarised as the
'ostrich' syndrome. In fact, they are the immature reactions
of a child and show us, as psychologists describe it,
'regressing' to an earlier stage of our development.

We cannot deal with problems by hiding our head under the
pillow, sulking or blaming others. The first step must be to
face the problem directly, and try to get to grips with it.

Recognising symptoms and identifying sources

We must spend time clarifying the source of stress, understanding as clearly as we can what causes it. If we do not, we can waste much effort in fruitless attempts to neutralise or remove it. Also, we should recognise the influence stress in one situation can have on another.

Sometimes stress can be eased by taking major steps such as changing jobs or moving house. If there are external sources of serious pressure that could be removed or at least lessened, it is sensible to identify whether they could be eliminated, before moving on to more complex solutions.

However, the problem can rarely be removed by a one-step solution. To remove, lessen or change it may also prove beyond our immediate resources. In some situations the only solution is to come to terms with the realities. In other situations a change in attitudes is called for.

It may be useful to think of strategies you have used, these may have involved:

- removing or reducing the outside pressure
- accepting that there are things that cannot be changed

Other strategies focus around changing:

- yourself
- relationships
- attitudes
- activities

In practice, all these are interrelated, but it is helpful to look at them one by one.

Yourself

We can sometimes be our own worst enemy!

As we grow, we develop complex responses to the whole range of external pressures on us, but in doing this, we create an equally complex system of internal pressures. By expecting more of ourselves than others, the internal pressures can often create greater stress than those that come from outside.

These internal pressures may centre around your need to be:

- efficient
- responsive
- competent
- successful
- effecting change
- appreciated

Therefore much of our stress can be self-induced – a product of the unrealistic expectations and demands we make on ourselves.

To reduce stress, all these internal pressures need to be put into perspective. First, we need to acknowledge that stress is a common and natural by-product of a demanding job. However, acknowledging this only goes some way to helping you cope with the pressures of the job, and responding to your particular needs to succeed.

It is important to recognise our limitations. There are a limited number of hours in the day and there is only so much that we can do within that time. There are also limits to our responsibility.

Throughout the process, it is important to keep a positive self-image and avoid self-fulfilling, negative prophecies.

How we see ourselves is based on the relationship between actual achievements and what we want and expect out of life. When our achievements exceed our expectations, our self-esteem rises significantly. To try this, establish a set of realistic and clearly defined goals on a daily, weekly, monthly or yearly basis. Monitor your achievement, and see how each success brings greater self-confidence.

Building our self-esteem involves reviewing all aspects of our lives, accepting the faults and insecurities and working to resolve them. As our self-esteem rises and we start to see ourselves more positively, we become more able to deal positively with the effects of stress.

Some simple guidelines are to be realistic, accept weaknesses and restrict changes.

Relationships

Think for a moment about the people you come into contact with in a week. They will fall into categories such as:

- colleagues
- friends
- family
- acquaintances

Think about which of the above groupings you would miss most if you were deprived of them and which you currently value the most. Just pausing momentarily and thinking can help us put things in perspective. From our contact with people and the relationships we develop, we gain an understanding of the type of person we are.

However, when we begin to feel the effects of stress, a common reaction can be likened to a state of siege. This siege can take various forms; it may mean distancing yourself from those closest to you. You begin the preparations for this state by ensuring that the environment is safe and free from any intruders. You may go so far as to create a closed environment free from all others, or appear to value outside relationships and priorities such as work and career at the expense of other personal relationships.

Both of these responses can be damaging. Distancing yourself from the people closest to you may be a defensive move, but may create other tensions in those relationships. Similarly, a safe environment can quickly change into one that is isolating. When you feel isolated, it becomes more difficult to create opportunities to meet people, and doing so requires much effort and courage.

Relationships are important to coping with stress because of the support they bring. However they can also be a strain; don't be afraid of ridding yourself of dead or damaging relationships.

It may help to talk through your worries. Do not be afraid to ask for direct help and to be receptive when it is offered.

Stress can also be increased by carrying the feelings of other people. We will look at this area in more detail tomorrow, but it is important to recognise that their problems are their responsibility and not yours, even if they have identified you as the person they want to talk to about them.

Attitudes

Your attitude to yourself and others can be altered by changing your aspirations. If we aim too high, inevitably some goals are missed. As a result, we come to regard ourselves as failures.

If, for example, your main motivator is to become the Prime Minister, though you have never been involved in politics, then the chances that you will ever achieve this position are low. However, it could be that your skills and capabilities would make you ideally suited to success in a totally different sphere, such as a football manager. If you continue to aspire to become the Prime Minister, stress will mount as the goal is seen to be unattainable.

It may help to look at the cause of stress in a different way, from a different perspective.

For example, think of a demanding situation which could put you under pressure and create stress, for example, a large business presentation. You have two choices here. You can add to the stress of the situation by worrying and becoming anxious, or change the way you look at it, so that you see its positive aspects. The presentation could be seen as exciting and challenging, rather than something that could go wrong. The change of perspective is likely to be both enabling and creative, or at the very least not as exhausting as the worry and anxiety.

Learn to work effectively. There are aspects of work decided by the employer or organisation which leave you with little control. If this causes stress, you should ask yourself whether the demands and pressures are real and reasonable.

Try to change the way you respond to pressure. While acknowledging that there are some things that you can change and others that you can't, the wisdom is to recognise which is which and resist the urge to attempt to change the impossible.

Your attitudes are central to coping with stress. Be realistic in your aspirations, expectations and goals, keeping all aspects of your life in perspective.

Activities

By reading and becoming more knowledgeable about stress, you have already taken the first steps towards self-help. From this point on you will be able to:

- identify your major sources of stress
- anticipate stressful periods and plan for them
- develop a repertoire of coping strategies and practise them

The strategy you choose will depend on the sources of stress. If you have identified yourself as a Type 'A', it may be that you decide to slow down, only attempting one thing at a time.

One of the first steps in developing stress relieving activities
is to take control of your time. You can do this by, for
example:

- taking the phone off the hook
- listing tasks you have to do
- leaving the office early
- planning priorities
- being disciplined about distractions

With your new-found time you can, at least temporarily,
withdraw from the pressure.

You may:

- follow a leisure pursuit
- relax
- watch TV
- take the day off

Alternatively, you can release emotional tension by engaging in physical activity, such as:

- swimming
- running
- squash
- digging the garden
- decorating

You also may need help from others in the form of good support and relevant training, setting realistic and consistent goals, being an effective communicator including people in decision making and clearly defined boundaries.

It is also important to develop a positive lifestyle, which may involve a range of things: maintaining the correct weight, regularly practising some form of exercise, engaging in some form of relaxation, using alcohol and caffeine in moderation, planning the use of our time, seeking out variety and change of pace, not dwelling on unimportant matters, expecting to succeed, approaching manageable projects one at a time and celebrating our successes.

Whilst no one simple measure is likely to be an immediate cure-all, removing even a minor problem may alleviate stress quite suddenly.

Target a key area of stress, but be flexible; if you experience difficulties you may need to move to another area in which you have more control.

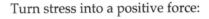

Turn stress into a positive force:

- Learn to say no
- Set realistic goals
- Delegate
- Organise and prioritise
- Seek help
- Be open
- Find a job which fits you

Helping others

Throughout the week you have developed an awareness of the existence of stress, its effects on health, behaviour, emotions and work. This awareness and understanding will not only benefit you but will help you become more adept at identifying stress in those around you.

Every day we need to interact with other people. Managers in particular are expected to establish and maintain relationships on many levels. But in doing so, managers have other, sometimes conflicting, duties. They must:

- lead
- make decisions
- control
- improve performance
- evaluate

In the context of our other roles and responsibilities, it is interesting to monitor our reaction to the suggestion of a role which involves helping others. It may be a role that you feel uncomfortable with because you recognise it as a skilled activity, because you feel that it could create conflicts or because you are too busy.

The role of helper is not one most of us will need to undertake constantly. If we did, we would suffer more rather than less stress. However, everyone adopts a helping role on occasions and like other roles, it is one that has its own range of skills.

> *Helping checklist*
> Think back over the last 24 hours and try to identify the ways in which you have helped other people:
> 1
> 2
> 3
> 4

Helping is a major part of a manager's role. You may, for instance, help others to:

- develop
- perform
- understand
- reach their potential

This role demands certain characteristics and skills, and it is these that we will look at in more detail today:

> *Helping*
> Characteristics   The 'being'
> Skills   The 'doing'

The 'being'

Before reading this book you may not have been aware of the signs which indicate that individuals need help. Managers are often so busy themselves that there is little time to recognise these signs or give others support or guidance.

However, recognising the signs and giving support and guidance are not as difficult as we may think, and the consequences of ignoring the symptoms and not confronting the problems can prove far more time consuming. This book by its very nature advocates a strategy of prevention rather than the all too common crisis intervention.

Relationships checklist
If you were asked, how would you honestly describe your relationships at work?

Superiors
Colleagues
Subordinates

What is the quality of these relationships dependent on?

We have already identified the fact that supportive relationships are essential to our well-being. The relationships you have at work may not be of the type that you would label supportive. However, at some point in your life you will have sought help in the form of advice, information or a listening ear. Think about the people you go to for help – what sort of people are they?

It is likely that they demonstrate certain characteristics:

- Honesty
- Respect
- Empathy

These are central to helping, and are often referred to as the 'essential characteristics'. We will look at all these in more detail in the following paragraphs.

Honesty

To be honest you must be yourself. We usually know instinctively when someone is acting or playing a role. We recognise the differences from their usual behaviour, and there are often subtle non-verbal indicators.

It is perhaps easier to understand honesty by looking at how people play roles. We all play roles, for a limited time and in specific settings. When we go home from work in the evenings, we may change our clothes and with them our behaviour, thus indicating the clear distinction between the two. We also learn to put on a 'front' either to impress others or to help us cope with difficult situations. This may involve consciously or unconsciously concealing parts of ourselves which we don't want to be seen – or which we don't want to acknowledge even to ourselves.

We often learn a new role by modelling ourselves on others.
It is when we stick to that model rather than being ourselves
that others are likely to see us as false. Honesty is not
something that can be turned on and off; it is a part of us.
We are genuine in our relationships when we are:

- spontaneous
- open
- consistent
- willing to share

Respect
Respect requires you to:

- believe the speaker
- give your undivided attention
- withhold judgements and criticism

We each experience life differently, seeing, feeling,
interpreting and enjoying things in our own unique ways.
This becomes obvious if two people relate an experience
they have had to a third person. The two descriptions may
seem to be of totally different events.

Believing and not judging are essential in developing trust
and respect in a helping relationship. There is nothing
worse than being told that our problem is not serious or, on
the other hand, that we have a very serious one and need
help. We must learn not to criticise, make judgements or
argue with what the person is saying. For many, this
represents a complete change of approach because at work

as managers and at home as parents, we spend much time teaching, persuading or even telling people to be different.

To respect and value others whatever their attitudes and actions is essential if we wish to help them. This requires that we give them our undivided attention, putting aside our own preoccupations. Treat them in a manner that indicates that their viewpoint is worth listening to.

Empathy
'Empathy' is the sharing or spontaneous understanding of someone else's feelings.

Because we are unique, we have unique views of the world. We use our senses to experience it and our minds to make meaning of these sensations. To be 'empathic' means putting aside our own view of the world and trying to experience how other people see theirs; putting yourself into their shoes and walk around in them momentarily.

In discussions generally, when there are differing points of view, we tend to assume that only one view can be right. To be a successful helper, we must understand that each person's experience is unique and valid for them.

Even those who demonstrate all the essential characteristics may not prove to be effective helpers if they lack the necessary skills. It is these we will focus on for the remainder of today.

The 'doing'

There are a number of possible methods of helping, which include:

- Listening
- Coaching
- Advising
- Organisational change
- Taking action
- Informing
- Support
- Counselling

Listening
Listening is an essential ingredient in each of the other methods of helping. However, listening is also a most effective method in its own right. To encourage those under stress to talk of their problems is often the golden key to unlock their own inner strength and resources.

Often the other person is not looking to us for a solution; they may just need us to listen and help them explore something aloud.

We often fail to understand what is being said because we tend to interpret rather than to listen. When we interpret, we are influenced by different factors:

- our point of view
- past experience
- present mood
- expectations

The mood we are in can also distort the reality of the situation. For example, if we are feeling angry about something, we are more likely to take offence at a petty remark, which at any other time would not have worried us and may even have gone unnoticed.

Coaching
We often associate coaching with sport. In the context of helping it means creating an environment whereby the individual can acquire the desired skills, improve their knowledge or develop their insights further.

Coaching may thus help someone to acquire an understanding of stress and go through a similar process to the one you have gone through in reading this book – learning what stress is, how to recognise it in ourselves and others, its sources, and the techniques and strategies for dealing with it.

A particular benefit of helping in this way is that once skills are acquired, they can be applied again and again, without our help!

Advising
On some occasions people may approach us wanting our advice, asking 'What should I do?' or 'What would you do?'. People often ask for advice from people they trust and respect and the act of doing so can significantly help a person without forcing them to take the offered solution. As an adviser we make suggestions based on our knowledge and understanding of the person and the problem. It is then for the individual to decide on their appropriateness.

Organisational change

Each day we have considered ways of making our individual work environment more healthy and less stressful.

However, some problems are best resolved by working on the structures rather than working with individuals. For example, a high turnover of employees suggests that something about the organisation needs to be changed, rather than the individuals in it.

We have already discussed ways of creating a more supportive environment: listening to employees, building structures in which they can participate, and being more responsive. Such moves can also increase the commitment of staff, with all its associated positive outcomes of improved communication, participation, empowerment and clarity of roles.

Taking action

This form of helping involves the helper working on behalf of the individual. It may take the form of practical help: writing a letter, a telephone call or contacting someone on their behalf.

We can often resolve issues immediately by this approach. However, the person we are helping does not learn and may not understand how and why we chose to act in that particular way, or even if it was the best course of action.

Informing

Information is a very necessary part of decision making. Simply informing someone about this book may be a great help! However, we are only likely to tell someone about this book if we find it helpful; it is a recommendation we are giving. This can often be the problem with information, as so little of it can be truly value free, and may particularly relate to you, your experiences and situation.

Collect information on sources of help both for yourself and others. Explore what is available from:

Your employer
Counselling at work for stressed workers is growing; this may be referred to as an Employee Assistance Programme. Other services may be available through personnel or occupational health departments.

The Health Service
Check with your doctor on the process of referral to counsellors and clinical psychologists. Some occupational health departments offer specialists in stress management.

Voluntary organisations
Addresses of local voluntary organisations should be available from your local Citizens Advice Bureau or Council for Voluntary Service.

A comprehensive listing of counselling services/individual counsellors is available from:

> British Association for Counselling
> 1 Regent Place, Rugby, CV21 2PJ
> Tel: 01788 578328

Two of the main organisations are:

> MIND – offers counselling on all aspects of mental health
> Relate – formerly The Marriage Guidance Council

Counselling

Counselling involves working with individuals and deals with the individual's feelings, thoughts and experiences, allowing them to develop at their own pace.

The previous strategies assume that the individual's needs are clearly known and have advanced to a stage where they can be addressed. In practice, we know from our own experience that this is often not the case. The importance of listening and hearing accurately has already been emphasised. Only by doing this can we understand the nature of the problem and develop appropriate actions or strategies.

The role of counsellor calls for much skill and time. We may not have sufficient of either. However, counselling skills used appropriately can help others to develop and as a result live more effectively.

In addition to the things to 'do' and 'be', there are also words of warning to those who would help others.

With your new-found knowledge and understanding, and the natural desire to apply them, you could be tempted to look for problems: don't! Beware of how you approach people: do not confront them directly. If they are stressed, they probably think they are doing a good job of disguising this from others and they are likely to feel threatened by such an approach.

We must also be clear that it is the other person's responsibility to do something about the problem, and that our intervention can only aid the process.

Also be aware of your own needs!

If we are approached by others for help, we must be aware of the demands that this makes on us and be sure to seek help for ourselves. If you don't pay attention to this balance or the support that you receive, your effectiveness and your ability to help will suffer. The needs vary for each person, but you may need more training or regular support.

Helping checklist
Try to answer the following questions.
- Are symptoms evident around you?

- How approachable and accessible are you?

- What kind of help could you supply?

- What other resources are available?

Today we have looked at helping others, but to help others, we must ourselves have reached a state of equilibrium.

Tomorrow we will begin to look at the prevention strategies that will help you develop a positive lifestyle and live effectively with stress.

Prevention

We are now at the end of the week and you will now have a good idea about the sources of stress. You will also have identified personality characteristics and life situations that make you more stress-prone and recognised ways to cope better with stress.

Stressful situations are an integral part of our everyday lives, but we can develop strategies to minimise the harm they cause. Today we will focus on these strategies, putting into practice all that we have become aware of, to move from coping with stress to preventing it. This is a two-stage process, which involves:

- monitoring
- managing

Monitoring

We must become aware of our own personal warning signs. Look back at what we discussed on Monday. The commonest signs of stress include:

- headaches
- stomach aches
- indigestion
- muscle tensions
- tearfulness
- desire to escape

Symptoms checklist
Think back to a recent stressful situation.
What symptoms did you exhibit?

When did these occur?

What was the probable cause of the stress?

Now turn to the future. Identify the incidents and situations that you look forward to with anxiety during the weeks and months to come. These may include a re-organisation, house move, redundancies at work, relationship breakdown, business presentation, etc.

From this you will be able to pinpoint types of situation and specific people who consistently seem to be implicated in your stressful experiences.

Identify whether they are:
- at a particular time
- in response to certain events
- when you are with certain people

Aim to be as specific as possible; collate all the facts. If you feel unhappy or emotional, is a problem lurking in the background? Learn to identify troublesome situations as problems.

To begin this process start a diary like the one opposite and try to maintain this over a four-week period.

From this format you should have a basis for establishing preventive strategies. Each incident and relationship can be managed if you are able to accurately identify and anticipate the problem.

Having identified what you should have done; the next step is to translate these 'shoulds' into future behaviours and actions.

Managing

You are now aware of what it is that makes you susceptible to stress, and are at the stage of making decisions on how you need to change.

DIARY

	Incident	People involved	What you did	What you should have done
Sunday				
Monday				
Tuesday				
Wednesday				
Thursday				
Friday				
Saturday				

The following paragraphs will give some guidance on how to achieve this:

Managing ourselves
- Forget the near misses
- Learn structured relaxation
- Treat yourself
- Sleep well
- Take sensible exercise
- Eat healthily
- Communicate effectively
- Seek help

Forget the near misses
It may be that from the monitoring, you have identified relatively few stressful incidents. For some, even a small number of problems – sometimes just one – can dominate their thinking and emotions. Professional sports people learn to leave behind their 'near misses' or 'bad shots', the 'might have beens'.

Checklist
Think back over the last month and try to identify the times when:
You felt you were criticised

You felt you were praised

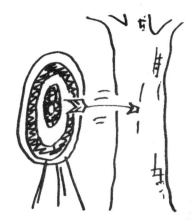

We are much more likely to hear criticism than praise. We may even interpret praise as criticism. For example, the manager who is praised for a report may question the quality of their previous reports, rather than accept the praise for the current one.

If we carry these criticisms around with us, we are perpetually at a disadvantage; we become weighted down with them and unable to focus on the next challenge. We will also be more likely to miss the opportunity to enjoy the much more frequent good moments that can in fact revive and relax us.

You will know of people who look for problems – they inevitably find them or maybe create them. Begin from today to look for opportunities rather than problems.

Learn structured relaxation
Regular relaxation is vital in managing the effects of stress, but the methods you choose must be effective.

A period of relaxation is a time to recharge your batteries.

There are a number of ways to practise relaxation, but they all have common factors.

Relaxation
Takes place in a
- quiet environment, free of stress-inducing reactions
The relaxer
- adopts a comfortable position
- focuses attention
- has a passive mental attitude

Such methods must be learnt and practised regularly, and should become a part of your life.

Some prefer to use established techniques such as yoga; others develop their own personal approach. Whatever the method, the benefits can be noticeable.

Treat yourself
Apart from structured relaxation, occasional treats are a great help. Everyone benefits from a good holiday, although even this has its risks, as we saw on Tuesday. But we do not need to wait for our annual leave. We can:

- pamper ourselves
- take a long bath
- go for a walk
- listen to music
- take a weekend away

Indulge in whatever you enjoy. Build these treats into your everyday life and reward yourself for progress and achievement.

Sleep well

You must ensure that you get sufficient sleep and rest. We all differ in the amount of sleep we need and in our ability to fall asleep quickly and sleep deeply.

This can be improved by:

- relaxing
- avoiding over-eating
- creating a comfortable environment

One of the effects of stress is exhaustion. This is not something that can be resolved by rest as, no matter how much rest you have, you may still feel tired. It is the quality of the rest that is important, therefore:

- resolve conflict
- put aside worries

By doing this you will benefit from good quality rest, ensuring that it is truly recuperative.

Take sensible exercise
Our minds are easily affected by a number of purely physical factors from drugs to diet and fatigue. Regular aerobic exercise can have a number of positive effects to minimise and prevent these effects.

Most managers live very sedentary lives. Indeed, much modern gadgetry, such as remote control televisions, washing machines, dishwashers, is designed to reduce physical effort and hence exercise.

One very inactive manager was shocked by the results of a health test, which showed him how unfit he was. Like so many of us, he:

- drove to and from work
- spent most of the day in his office
- passed most evenings resting in a comfortable armchair in front of the television.

The test results had a massive effect on him and he started to exercise regularly. Consequently, not only did he feel much better, but his whole outlook on life had in some way lightened; he had more energy and his feelings of fatigue had largely disappeared. Generally, more physical exercise reduces our weight and improves our physical health.

Try different forms of exercise. It may take a few attempts before you find one you like, that fits with you and your lifestyle.

Eat healthily
Good nutrition is a help in reducing susceptibility to stress. A balanced diet of protein and carbohydrates, including fewer foods that are high in sugar and fat content, will soon enhance our general health and feelings of well-being.

Be aware of what you eat. Is there an imbalance? If so, how could you change this?

Change
- eating patterns
- routines
- types of food

Communicate effectively
In managing stress we must ensure that our communication is clear and accurate. Have you ever walked away from someone, wishing you had not said something or knowing that you have been misunderstood? We must aim to:

- speak clearly
- say what we mean
- be specific
- listen carefully
- clarify our understanding

Begin by clarifying misunderstandings as they arise, expressing feelings, talking, writing and venting frustrations. Also:

- check others' understanding of what you say
- don't leave matters in the air

Such an approach will not only help us to reduce stress, but will also help those with whom we come into contact.

Communicating effectively can also build the relationships that will give us long-term support.

Seek help
Everything we have discussed so far is aimed at building our resilience and lowering our reactivity. Managing our stress may also involve changing our outlook and rethinking many aspects of our lives. You may need help to do this.

Seek help though your existing networks of friends, colleagues and family. Re-establish these networks if necessary. Or explore other avenues, such as professional help:

- counsellors
- therapists
- psychologists

You will be aware from your reading yesterday of the different types of help available. Think carefully about what type of help would be useful to you.

Seek Help
Decide what kind of help is needed. This may fall into the following categories:

One to one   Counsellors/therapists/psychologists. Individuals and organisations offer confidential services on commercial and charitable basis. Try the British Association of Counselling, address on p. 75.

Self-help   A wide range of self-help groups exists. For more information refer to the Voluntary Agencies Directory, published by Bedford Square Press, 26 Bedford Square, London WC1B 3HU.

Training   The training you need may fall into one of the following categories:

Stress management
Personal effectiveness
Assertiveness
Meditation

Be sure that you are clear about your training needs.

Reading   Many books exist on this and related issues (see Further Reading on p. 96).

Remember that help doesn't only come from others. To prevent stress in the longer term it is essential that you help yourself in what you say and do, by developing habits that support you.

The following checklist will help.

Self-help action checklist
Follow the sequence below.

* Identify problems

* Identify solutions
  — brainstorm
  — be creative
  — be specific

* Consider preferred solutions. They must be:
  — practical
  — realistic

> — achievable
> — manageable
> and always in keeping with your
> — values
> — environment
>
> • Action:
> — plan
> — rehearse
> — act

It helps to make a contract with yourself to change and a commitment to persist. This may be written, setting out exactly what you have decided to do and by when. Having done this, you can:

> • record your progress
> • reward yourself

Both are important in keeping motivated. A record of progress and achievements can help to maintain our motivation and sense of progress when the going gets tough. As we mentioned previously today, rewards are an important part of the process; you know what you like and enjoy – reward yourself with these things.

We may know what we should do and even know how to do it, but never get round to it, for fear of the consequences. Change does involve risk and the outcomes may not always be what we want or expect. Managing your stress may not only require you to change, but also to view your life and experiences from a different perspective.

If you sit in the same old position year in, year out, your outlook will be the same. By changing that position, everything appears different; you are seeing things from a different perspective, in a different light and maybe seeing things for the first time as your vision has been blocked.

Your future is in your hands. Move towards preventing stress by minimising it at all levels, for:

- yourself
- organisations
- society

MINIMISING STRESS

For ourselves

Ensure
- good person/job fit

Develop
- sensible, rational beliefs and attitudes
- skills and behaviours
- good social support network

Learn
- to relax
- to use leisure time profitably
- to keep as physically healthy as you can

For our organisations

Develop
- jobs with clear job descriptions
- good communication systems
- a sense of involvement

Provide
- help with problems
- support
- adequate resources

For society at large

Encourage
- greater sharing of feelings and support
- co-operation

Abandon
- glamorous image of stress

Believe
- stress can kill

If we have recognised a need to deal with stress in our life
we have taken the first important step towards successfully
overcoming it. But the recognition needs to be followed by
determination and patience. There must be a determination
to face truths about ourself and make the necessary changes
that will provide staying power when the going gets tough.
In addition there must be the patience to understand that
worthwhile change does not come about quickly. It is a
long-term process which is prone to setbacks and
diversions.

Prevention
- accept yourself as you are
- avoid blaming others
- avoid blaming your environment
- take responsibility

However, if we are suffering serious stress, change isn't an
optional extra; our happiness and well-being depend on it.

When it comes, it will bring with it an easing of pressures, profound changes in personality and mood, and an approach to life which benefits both us and those we work and live with.

■ F U R T H E R   R E A D I N G ■

Coping with Stress at Work, J.M. Atkinson, Thorsons, 1988.

Employee Assistance Programmes and Workplace Counselling, J. Berridge, C.L. Cooper and C. Highley, Chichester, John Wiley and Sons, 1997.

Living with Stress, C.L. Cooper, R.D. Cooper and L.H. Eaker, Penguin, 1988.

Managing Pressure at Work, H Froggart and P. Stamp, BBC Books, 1991.

Managing Stress, U. Markham, Element Books, 1989.

Managing Workplace Stress, S. Cartwright and C.L. Cooper, London, Sage, 1997.

Organisational Stress and Preventative Management, J.C. Quick and J.D. Quick, New York, McGraw Hill, 1984.

Positive Stress Management, P.E. Makin and P.A. Lindley, Kogan Page, 1991.

Stress and the Manager: Making It Work for You, K. Albrecht, Prentice-Hall, 1979.

Stressful Life Events, Personality, Health: An Enquiry into Hardiness, S. Kobasa, Journal of Personality and Social Psychology, Vol 37, 1979.

Stresswise, T. Looker and O. Gregson, Hodder and Stoughton, 1989.

Thriving on Stress, J. Cranwell-Ward, Routledge, 1990.

Type A Behaviour and Your Heart, M. Friedman and R. Rosenman, Knopf, 1974.

Understanding Stress, Consumers Association/Hodder and Stoughton, 1988.